THE BEST OF
FRANK LOESSER

FRANK MUSIC CORP.

Exclusive Distributor:
BRADLEY PUBLICATIONS
a division of RBR Communications, Inc.
43 West 61 Street
New York, N.Y. 10023

april·blackwood
publications

Dedication from Cy Coleman

Nobody slept around Frank Loesser. His presence charged the air. He combined his creative musical genius with an extraordinary flair for business. His endless energy and restless mind was always on the lookout for new and different avenues of expression. He was an enthusiastic supporter of newcomers and new ideas.

It was in this context that I first met Frank Loesser. I had a brand new trio and played nightly in an out-of-the-way night spot called the Shelbourne Lounge. Frank would come in to see me night after night and would bring in a continuous parade of celebrities to come hear me. I, in turn, became fascinated with his work and started to feature some of the wonderful treasures of his remarkable catalogue.

Later, when I became more involved in theatre writing, I felt Frank's pervasive influence with the people I was working with. Bob Fosse, who had worked with Frank, had adopted the "Loesser Technique" of auditioning singers. Namely, he would take Irving Berlin's song "Blue Skies", have the auditioning singer do the first eight bars and then keep raising the key one half step at a time until the singer would reach the top of his or her range (usually screeching). Bob used this technique so much that when a friend of mine was auditioning for Bob I put together an arrangement of "Blue Skies" for her that went up to the very top and down to the very bottom of her vocal range. She got the job.

Knowing Bob Fosse's high regard and genuine affection for Frank, I called him and asked him to contribute a few thoughts to this piece. Bobby contemplated a little while, then he said, "Besides his overwhelming talent, Frank was one of the most unpredictable men I have ever met. I worked with him twice; the first show was an enormous hit (HOW TO SUCCEED IN BUSINESS WITHOUT REALLY TRYING). During that time he was obstinate, tough and very often unyielding. The second show (PLEASURES AND PALACES) was unfortunately a failure. In the face of adversity he was kind, understanding and generous. You could never guess what his reaction to a situation might be but you always knew it would be right."

Frank Loesser combined his musical, lyrical, and business genius with the finest qualities of a compassionate and humane human being. Wherever Frank is auditioning now, you know there's got to be "Blue Skies from now on" higher, higher, higher.

Cy Coleman

Biography:
FRANK LOESSER (June 29, 1910 - July 28, 1969)

When you think of Frank Loesser, what comes to mind is the immediacy of his music and lyrics. Because his attitude towards life was so contemporary, realistic and energetic, he did not permit nostalgia to enter into his vocabulary and today, his creative genius and relevance are as vital as ever.

And such energy! He rocked Broadway and the rest of the world with his five distinguished works for the musical theatre, WHERE'S CHARLEY?, GUYS AND DOLLS, THE MOST HAPPY FELLA, GREENWILLOW and the Pulitzer Prize-winning, HOW TO SUCCEED IN BUSINESS WITHOUT REALLY TRYING, which would have been enough by ordinary standards but Frank was not ordinary in any sense of the word. As a very young man, he had already run the gamut of the Hollywood scene, pouring out wry and witty hits for the screen such as the Academy Award-winning BABY, IT'S COLD OUTSIDE to patriotic anthems like PRAISE THE LORD AND PASS THE AMMUNITION, as well as delicious ballads as the lovely SPRING WILL BE A LITTLE LATE THIS YEAR. Then later, he returned to Hollywood for his great HANS CHRISTIAN ANDERSEN score.

You could say that he was "born to the manner" since his father was a respected teacher of classical piano in New York City where Frank was born and reared, and his older brother Arthur not only was a celebrated pianist, musicologist and music critic but also headed the Cleveland Institute of Music and became one of the leading piano pedagogues in the country. Rather than gaining his ability through any formal training, Frank simply absorbed music and his brilliance was so apparent on all levels that even in high school, he was accepted into a special school for students of exceptional intelligence (PS 165, Townsend Harris High School).

Actually, there was ostensibly a non-musical hiatus in Frank's career during the Depression when he did just about everything; selling newspaper ad space, covering the knitted fashion field for Women's Wear Daily, working as a process server and lastly, being city editor of a short-lived newspaper in New Rochelle, N.Y. It all touched him and anecdotes from these experiences were stored in his portable mental reference library - he never forgot or missed a moment. While doing all of these things, Frank had enough "spare time" to write songs, acts, sketches and radio scripts. Since he did not require more than four hours sleep at a stretch, he was sufficiently refreshed by an intermittent cat-nap and his unrelenting dynamism never waned. In these early years, he wrote with William Schuman, who later emerged as a distinguished classical composer and moving force behind the creation of Lincoln Center for the Performing Arts. Their first published collaboration was a song called IN LOVE WITH THE MEMORY OF YOU. Of this opus, Schuman remarked in retrospect, "Frank Loesser has written hits with Hoagy Carmichael, Burton Lane, Jule Styne and other Hollywood grand-dukes but I have the distinction of having written a flop with him!"

When Frank went on to Hollywood in 1937, he wrote his first film hit, THE MOON OF MANAKOORA (with Alfred Newman), immortalized by Dorothy Lamour in the picture, HURRICANE. This was only the beginning of his film-writing era and he continued to create songs for more than sixty movies. After returning to New York and embarking on the Broadway scene, the ever-astute businessman that he innately was, convinced him that he should combine the artistic and administrative sides of his nature and he formed his own music publishing company, aptly named FRANK MUSIC CORP. It was not enough for him to handle merely his own materials because he felt that the primary purpose of his company was to discover and develop the talent of young, new composers and lyricists in all phases of the popular idiom and he attracted them from all over the country. He built his company to become a major force in American music publishing, encompassing every area such as printing music editions, licensing of secondary rights and developing artist/writers as well as structuring the company to run in his own precise and inimitable way. Later the company was sold to the Eastman companies where it is still thriving.

Still, all of this activity was not the end of Frank's interest and his personal life was centered around his family. In 1959, he married soprano Jo Sullivan, who starred in THE MOST HAPPY FELLA, THREE PENNY OPERA and other Broadway musicals as well as television specials. He was the very proud father of four children; Hannah and Emily with his last wife, Jo, and Susan and John from his earlier marriage to the former Lynn Garland.

Although Frank Loesser died in July of 1969, he left us the fruits of his undying spirit and vitality through his music and lyrics for the over fifteen hundred songs that he wrote. He was and is a man for our times.

In Hollywood with Susan Loesser, his first child.

Next to Kermut Bloomgarden during rehearsal for *The Most Happy Fella*.

With Billy Morse from *How To Succeed At Business Without Really Trying.*

Watching the filming of *Hans Christian Andersen.*

Frank Loesser in his only film, *Red, Hot & Blue.*

. . . as a gangster, with his two henchmen.

. . . with Betty Hutton.

Contents By Source

GREENWILLOW

GUYS AND DOLLS

HOW TO SUCCEED IN BUSINESS WITHOUT REALLY TRYING

THE MOST HAPPY FELLA

WHERE'S CHARLEY?

HANS CHRISTIAN ANDERSEN

ABOUT FACE

NEPTUNE'S DAUGHTER

THE HURRICANE

ROSEANNA McCOY

SEE HERE, PRIVATE HARGROVE

Contents
(Alphabetical)

Faraway Boy

From the Musical Production "Greenwillow"

by
FRANK LOESSER

Gideon Briggs, I Love You

From the Musical Production "Greenwillow"

by
FRANK LOESSER

The Music Of Home

From the Musical Production "Greenwillow"

by
FRANK LOESSER

Never Will I Marry

From the Musical Production "Greenwillow"

by
FRANK LOESSER

Greenwillow Christmas

Moderate

From the Musical Production "Greenwillow"

by
FRANK LOESSER

Chorus Ensemble

Walking Away Whistling

From the Musical Production "Greenwillow"

by
FRANK LOESSER

But a wan-der-ing man is a wan-der-ing man, And there's o-ceans and moun-tains out there.
But a wan-der-ing man is a wan-der-ing man, And he'd nev-er rest eas-y in town. } He'll be

Walk-ing A-way___ Whist-ling,— whist-ling,— whist-ling,—

Walk-ing A-way___ Whist-ling,— whist-ling,— come dawn.

dawn. Whist-ling, whist-ling, and gone. ___

Summertime Love

From the Musical Production "Greenwillow"

by
FRANK LOESSER

34

37

Adelaide

From the Motion Picture "Guys and Dolls"

by
FRANK LOESSER

pho- ny and I'm a fake, She wants five chil-dren to start. Five's a dif- fi-cult point to make! But

Refrain (*with a sentimental lilt*)

Ad- e - laide, Ad- e - laide, Ev- er lov- in' Ad- e - laide is

tak- in' a chance on me. Tak- in' a chance__ I'll be re-

spect- a- ble and nice, Give up the cards and dice And go for shoes and rice! So,

I've Never Been In Love Before

From the Musical Production "Guys and Dolls"

by
FRANK LOESSER

43

Adelaide's Lament

From the Musical Production "Guys and Dolls"

by
FRANK LOESSER

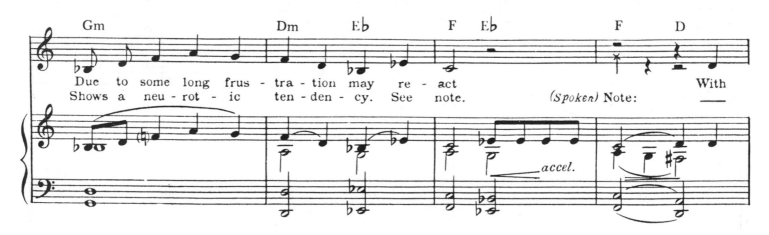

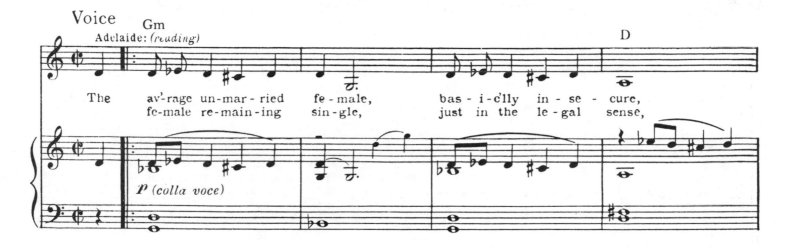

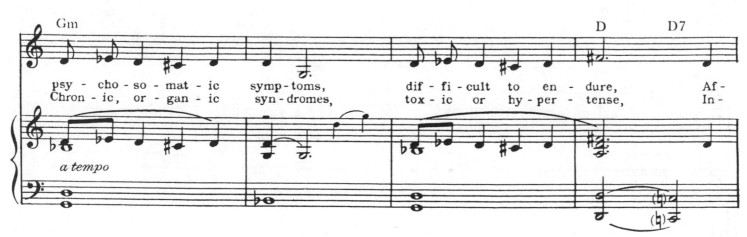

45

48

A Woman In Love

From the Motion Picture "Guys and Dolls"

by
FRANK LOESSER

More I Cannot Wish You

From the Musical Production "Guys and Dolls"

by
FRANK LOESSER

54

55

Follow The Fold

From the Musical Production "Guys and Dolls"

by
FRANK LOESSER

Luck Be A Lady

From the Musical Production "Guys and Dolls"

by
FRANK LOESSER

yet be-fore this eve-ning is ov-er you might give me the brush.__ You

might for-get your man-ners, you might re-fuse to stay, And so the best that I can do is

Brightly

pray._____

Chorus

Luck be a la-dy to-night _____

62

Nev - er get out of my sight_____

Stick with me ba - by I'm the fel - low you came in with,

Luck be a la - dy, luck be a la - dy, Luck be a la - dy to-night.

Sit Down You're Rockin' The Boat

From the Musical Production "Guys and Dolls"

by
FRANK LOESSER

Chorus with a beat

Take Back Your Mink

From the Musical Production "Guys and Dolls"

by
FRANK LOESSER

Pet Me, Poppa

From the Motion Picture "Guys and Dolls"

by
FRANK LOESSER

Adelaide and Dolls:

You know you've been mean to me And you know, when you're mean to me, How it al-ways makes me want to roam. _____ And you know there's a dan-ger That some gen-tle stran-ger Might pick me up and make me feel at home. _____ So;

Refrain (with a beat)

72

Sue Me

From the Musical Production "Guys and Dolls"

by
FRANK LOESSER

The Oldest Establshed

From the Musical Production "Guys and Dolls"

by
FRANK LOESSER

Bright tempo

Guys And Dolls

From the Musical Production "Guys and Dolls"

by
FRANK LOESSER

My Time Of Day

From the Musical Production "Guys and Dolls"

by
FRANK LOESSER

A Bushel And A Peck

From the Musical Production "Guys and Dolls"

by
FRANK LOESSER

you _____ a-bout you _____ 'Cause

I love you a bu-shel and a peck y' bet your pur-ty neck I do_

(Optional Duet)
Doo - dle oo - dle oo - dle Doo - dle oo - dle oo - dle a-

doo - dle oo - dle oo - dle ooo._

If I Were A Bell

From the Musical Production "Guys and Dolls"

by
FRANK LOESSER

1.Ask me how do I feel, Ask me now that we're co-sy and cling-ing
2.how do I feel From this Chem-is-try les-son I'm learn-ing

Well sir, all I can say is if I were a bell I'd be
Well sir, all I can say is if I were a bridge I'd be

ring-ing.
burn-ing.

From the mo-ment we kissed to-nite
Yes, I knew my mor-ale would crack

Marry The Man Today

From the Musical Production "Guys and Dolls"

by
FRANK LOESSER

94

I'll Know

From the Musical Production "Guys and Dolls"

by
FRANK LOESSER

Fugue For Tinhorns

From the Musical Production "Guys and Dolls"

by
FRANK LOESSER

104

Three Cornered Tune

Based on "Fugue For Tinhorns" from the Musical Production "Guys and Dolls"

by
FRANK LOESSER

107

108

109

Wonderful Copenhagen

From the Motion Picture "Hans Christian Andersen"

by
FRANK LOESSER

Anywhere I Wander

From the Motion Picture "Hans Christian Andersen"

by
FRANK LOESSER

Refrain

Ben marcato

I'm Hans Christian Andersen

From the Motion Picture "Hans Christian Andersen"

by
FRANK LOESSER

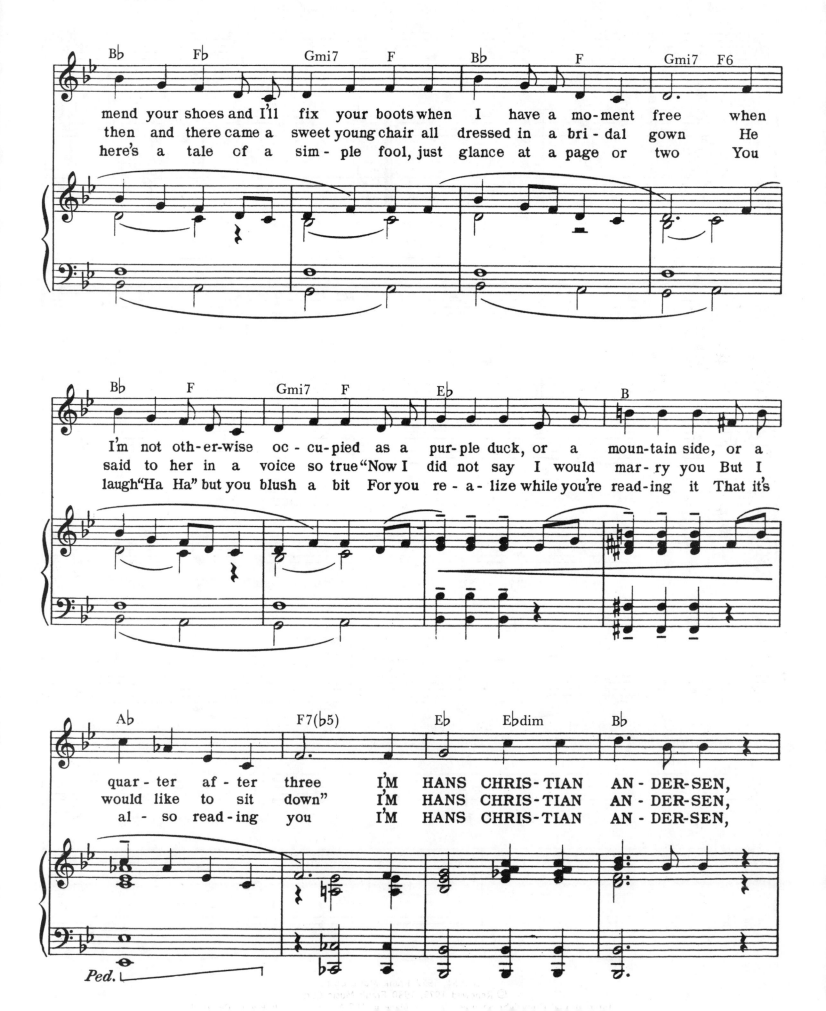

117

The Ugly Duckling

From the Motion Picture "Hans Christian Andersen"

by
FRANK LOESSER

Lightly with a Waddle

Lyrics:
There once was an ug-ly duck-ling with feath-ers all stub-by and brown and the oth-er birds, in so man-y words, said Get out of town *(Quack like an angry Duck)* get out, get out get out of town. And he

121

124

The Inch Worm

From the Motion Picture "Hans Christian Andersen"

by
FRANK LOESSER

Thumbelina

From the Motion Picture "Hans Christian Andersen"

by
FRANK LOESSER

Thum - be - li - na, what's the dif - f'rence if you're ver - y small?

When your heart is full of love you're nine feet tall.

2. Though nine feet

tall.

The King's New Clothes

From the Motion Picture "Hans Christian Andersen"

by
FRANK LOESSER

135

No Two People

From the Motion Picture "Hans Christian Andersen"

by
FRANK LOESSER

141

Brotherhood Of Man

From the Musical Production "How To Succeed In Business Without Really Trying"

by
FRANK LOESSER

With a Handclapper Spiritual Feeling

146

I Believe In You

From the Musical Production "How To Succeed In Business Without Really Trying"

by
FRANK LOESSER

150

151

Paris Original

From the Musical Production "How To Succeed In Business Without Really Trying"

by
FRANK LOESSER

157

How To Succeed In Business Without Really Trying

From the Musical Production "How To Succeed In Business Without Really Trying"

by
FRANK LOESSER

With Ambition

How to ap-ply for a job, How to ad-vance from the mail room, How to sit down at a desk, How to dic-tate mem-o-ran-dums, How to de-vel-op ex-ec-u-tive style,

159

A Secretary Is Not A Toy

From the Musical Production "How To Succeed In Business Without Really Trying"

by
FRANK LOESSER

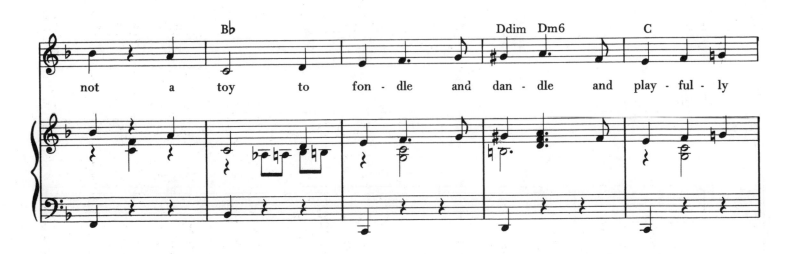

163

A sec-re-tar-y is not a thing

wound by key, pulled by string. Her pad is to write in, and

not spend the night in... If that's what you plan to en-

joy. No! The

Rap on piano (like a typewriter)

Grand Old Ivy

From the Musical Production "How To Succeed In Business Without Really Trying"

by
FRANK LOESSER

Interlude

Rosemary

From the Musical Production "How To Succeed In Business Without Really Trying"

by
FRANK LOESSER

Rose - ma - ry was the
Rose - ma - ry, just i - mag - ine ____
Rose - ma - ry, there is

if we kissed... what a cre - scen - do. ____

Not to be missed.

As for the

won - der - ful mu - sic in the ver - y

179

Rose Jay Pierre - pont, _____ ma - ry, there is won - der - ful mu - sic in the ver - y sound _____ of your name. _____

Happy To Keep His Dinner Warm

From the Musical Production "How To Succeed In Business Without Really Trying"

by
FRANK LOESSER

183

Cinderella, Darling

From the Musical Production "How To Succeed In Business Without Really Trying"

by
FRANK LOESSER

192

Coffee Break

From the Musical Production "How To Succeed In Business Without Really Trying"

by
FRANK LOESSER

Love From A Heart Of Gold

From the Musical Production "How To Succeed In Business Without Really Trying"

by
FRANK LOESSER

The Company Way

From the Musical Production "How To Succeed In Business Without Really Trying"

by
FRANK LOESSER

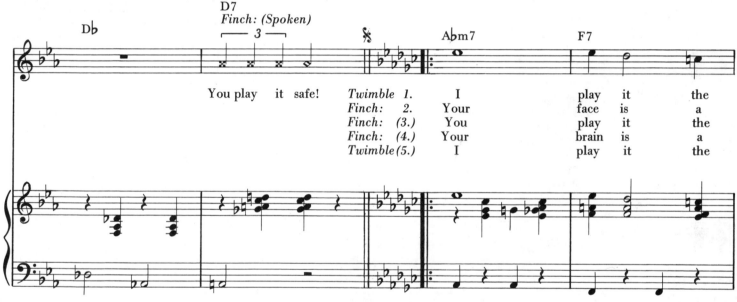

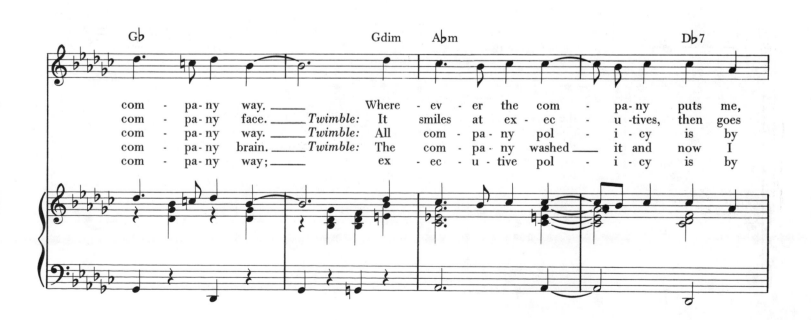

The Most Happy Fella

Excerpt from Act I Scene II of "The Most Happy Fella"

by
FRANK LOESSER

210

211

Big D

Excerpt from Act II Scene I of "The Most Happy Fella"

by
FRANK LOESSER

214

Standing On The Corner

Excerpt from Act I Scene II of "The Most Happy Fella"

by
FRANK LOESSER

Don't Cry

Excerpt from Act I Scene IV of "The Most Happy Fella"

by
FRANK LOESSER

My Heart Is So Full Of You

Excerpt from Act II Scene IV of "The Most Happy Fella"

by
FRANK LOESSER

Joey, Joey, Joey

Excerpt from Act I Scene II of "The Most Happy Fella"

by
FRANK LOESSER

226

I Like Ev'rybody

Excerpt from Act II Scene IV of "The Most Happy Fella"

by
FRANK LOESSER

232

Somebody, Somewhere

Excerpt from Act I Scene I of "The Most Happy Fella"

by
FRANK LOESSER

Warm All Over

Excerpt from Act II Scene III of "The Most Happy Fella"

by
FRANK LOESSER

Once In Love With Amy

From the Musical Production "Where's Charley?"

by
FRANK LOESSER

boom, boom, boom, boom, boom, boom, boom, boom, boom ____ from then on, For

Chorus

once in love with A-my,____ Al-ways in love with A-my.____

Ev-er and ev-er fas-cin-at-ed by 'er, Sets your heart a-fire__ to stay.

Once you're kissed by A-my,____ Tear up your list, i'ts A-my.____

Ply her with bon-bons, po-et-ry and fow-ers, Moon a mil-lion hours_a - way.____ You

My Darling, My Darling

From the Musical Production "Where's Charley?"

by
FRANK LOESSER

Pernambuco

From the Musical Production "Where's Charley?"

by
FRANK LOESSER

Samba *Moderato*

PER - NAM - BU - CO, _____ un - be - liev - a - ble town _____ Where the crops go to seed ___ and the bank ___ Is in need ___ of fi - nanc ___ - ing, ___ Still, the peo - ple keep danc - ing. _____ PER - NAM - BU - CO, _____

245

Where's Charley?

From the Musical Production "Where's Charley?"

by
FRANK LOESSER

249

Lovelier Than Ever

From the Musical Production "Where's Charley?"

by
FRANK LOESSER

The New Ashmolean Marching Society and Students Conservatory Band

From the Musical Production "Where's Charley?"

by
FRANK LOESSER

Make A Miracle

From the Musical Production "Where's Charley?"

by
FRANK LOESSER

264

One Little WAC

From the Motion Picture "About Face"

Lyric by
FRANK LOESSER

Music by
EDDIE DUNSTEDTER

The Moon Of Manakoora

From the Motion Picture "The Hurricane"

Lyric by
FRANK LOESSER

Music by
ALFRED NEWMAN

270

In My Arms

From the Motion Picture "See Here, Private Hargrove"

by
FRANK LOESSER
and
TED GROUYA

EXTRA CHORUSES

2

In My Arms, In My Arms
Ain't I never gonna get a girl in my arms?
In My Arms, In My Arms
Ain't I never gonna get a bundle of charms?
Comes the dawn, I'll be gone,
And I thank you for the many letters you'll write.
As for something nice and cute and female,
I'll never get it in the V-Mail,
Gimme a girl in my arms tonight.

3

In My Arms, In My Arms
Ain't I never gonna get a girl in my arms?
In My Arms, In My Arms
Ain't I never gonna get a bundle of charms?
Comes the dawn I'll be gone,
I'll be headin' for the very thick of the fight,
You can wine and dine and cigarette me,
But if you really wanna get me,
Gimme a girl in my arms tonight.

4

In My Arms, In My Arms
Ain't I never gonna get a girl in my arms?
In My Arms, In My Arms
Ain't I never gonna get a bundle of charms?
Comes the dawn I'll be gone,
Now does anybody wanna please treat me right?
You can keep your shavin' cream and lotion,
If I'm a-gonna cross the ocean,
Gimme a girl in my arms tonight.

Baby, It's Cold Outside

From the Motion Picture "Neptune's Daughter"

by
FRANK LOESSER

Roseanna

From the Motion Picture "Roseanna McCoy"

by
FRANK LOESSER

On A Slow Boat To China

by
FRANK LOESSER

All Is Forgiven
(And All Is Forgotten)

by
FRANK LOESSER

What Are You Doing New Year's Eve

by
FRANK LOESSER

A Tune For Humming

by
FRANK LOESSER

Hoop~Dee~Doo
(Polka)

Lyric by
FRANK LOESSER

Music by
MILTON DeLUGG

293

Doesn't That Mean Anything To You

Lyric by
FRANK LOESSER

Music by
BOB EMMERICH

Have I Stayed Away Too Long

by
FRANK LOESSER

298

Goo Goo G'Da

Lyric by
BILLY FRISCH
RAYMOND LEVEEN
FRANK LOESSER

Music by
ERNEST BREUER

Junk Man

Lyric by
FRANK LOESSER

Music by
JOSEPH MEYER

The Feathery Feelin'

by
FRANK LOESSER

A Tree In Tipperaray

Lyric by
FRANK LOESSER

Music by
IRVING ACTMAN

The Last Thing I Want is Your Pity

by
FRANK LOESSER

What Do You Do In The Infantry

by
FRANK LOESSER

March (regulation Army tempo — 120 paces per minute)

what do you do in the In - fan - try? You march, you march, you march!

What do you do in the In - fan - try? You hike, you hike, you hike.

What do you get in the In - fan - try? A left and right o - blique._____ The
(pronounced O-blike)

son - of - a - gun in the Sig - nal Corps is trav - el - ing on a bike,_____ And

Rodger Young

by
FRANK LOESSER

320

Spring Will Be A Little Late This Year

by
FRANK LOESSER

322

323

Wave To Me, My Lady

by
WILLIAM STEIN
and
FRANK LOESSER

Just Another Polka

by
FRANK LOESSER
and
MILTON DeLUGG

Polka tempo

Voice

Bb

This is JUST AN-OTH-ER POL-KA, JUST AN-OTH-ER POL-KA, But

F7   Cm   Cm7   F7

oh what a {girl {guy in my arms. ____ Am I in Heav-en since we met?

C7   F7

Is this the Phil-har-mon-ic play-ing Ro-me-o and Ju-li-et?(shout)No!

328

Trio

danc - ing with an an - gel, ____ with an an - gel, an

an - gel, an an - gel. ____ Oh yes I'm danc - ing with an an - gel, ____

____ That's why the band is sound-ing bet - ter from the mo - ment that I
____ And there is Heav - en in the rhy - thm ev - 'ry min - ute that I'm

met her 'Cause I'm danc - ing with an an - gel, ____ with an
with 'im

Playing piano for children in the 60's at the same camp he attended as a child.

In the army.

APPENDIX